49

£1

THIS ANNUAL NEEDS YOU!

Of course I know you! You're my greatest fan. (One of millions, actually, but modesty forbids me from mentioning that fact; besides, I like you to feel special.) Welcome to my latest annual – it's my fifth and finest!

Inside you'll find three brand new prose stories, an original poem and a special cat story that, like Jon's wardrobe, always moves me to tears. On the information front, there are feature articles about my two friends, teddy bears and mice. (I recommend showing the mice pictures to your mum or big sister to see if they can break the world high-jump record.) And if you want to work your brain (perish the thought!), there are three fiendishly clever puzzles, a not-too-difficult/not-too-easy quiz and a totally original board game to play with a friend.

I could go on to mention the four eye-catching posters, the astonishing food facts, my invaluable advice about Christmas and all the pages of classic strips, but I won't because you must be keener to get your teeth into this annual than I am to get mine into a deep-pan lasagne. So go for it, gentle reader!

IF YOU DON'T INDULGE YOURSELF . . .
NOBODY WILL!

GARFIELD
ANNUAL

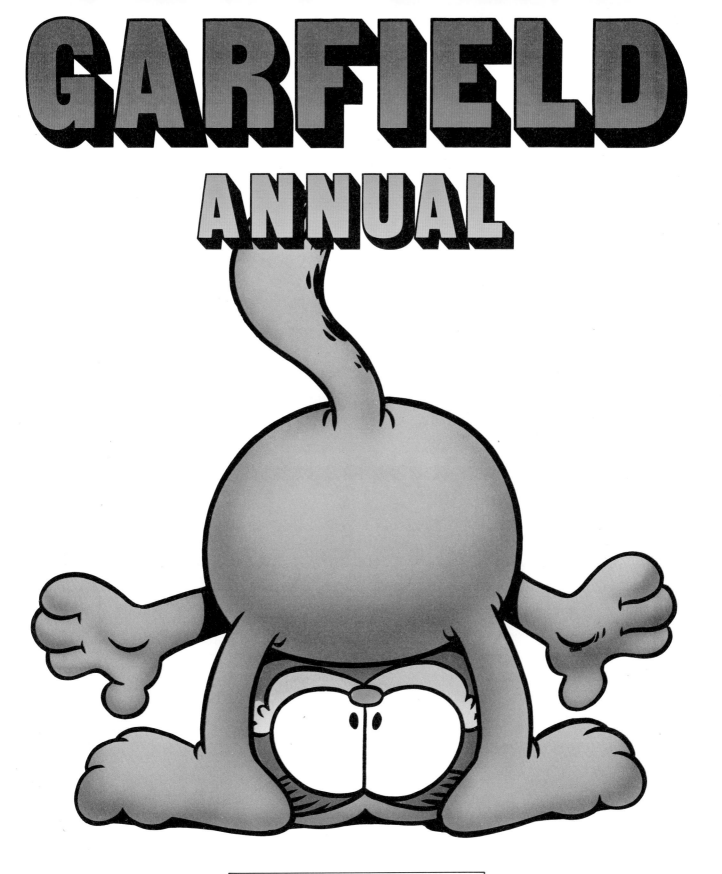

Created by
JiM DAViS

Written by
Gordon Volke

RAVETTE BOOKS

Contents

Printed and bound for Ravette Books Limited, 8 Clifford Street, London W1,
an Egmont Company, by Proost International Bookproduction, Belgium.

ISBN 1 85304 576 4

The FAT TUM of the Opera

"Do you like Pavarotti, Garfield?" asked Jon.

"I like all Italian food," said Garfield.

"How about Cosi Fan Tutte?" added Jon.

"Can't stand ice-cream with bits in it," murmured Garfield.

"It's opera, Garfield!" exclaimed Jon.

"I know, I know," snapped Garfield, turning on the TV to express his boredom. Jon turned if off again.

"I'm heavily into opera," Jon announced, "and I've bought two tickets for tonight's show in town. I'm taking Liz."

"Bet you're not," thought Garfield.

Just then, the phone rang. It was Liz to say she had to work late.

"Bingo!" grinned Garfield.

"Never mind," cried Jon bravely, "I'll ask someone else."

Two hours later, Jon had exhausted every name in his little black book and several dozen more from the telephone directory.

"There's only one person left," he said.

"You can't take Arlene," exclaimed Garfield. "She's waitressing tonight to pay for my Christmas presents."

"I'll take *you*, Garfield," smiled Jon.

That evening, Garfield sprawled in his seat at the opera house, snoring like a pig with 'flu.

"Someone tell that woman in the helmet to stop screeching," he muttered. "She keeps waking me up."

"Only another hour to the end of the first act," whispered Jon. "Then there are two more glorious acts to come."

"I won't make it," groaned Garfield.

At last, the interval arrived and Garfield sloped off on his own. He terrorised the usherette into giving him the entire contents of her refreshment tray, then wandered down to the orchestra pit and picked up the conductor's baton.

"How about a chorus of 'Here Comes Garfield' to liven up the proceedings?" he grinned.

A burley steward appeared, picked Garfield up by the scruff of the neck and dumped him outside the theatre.

"That's no way to treat a music lover!" protested Garfield.

Garfield looked round for some way to get back to his seat.

"Not that I fancy any more opera," he mumbled, "but Jon said something about supper afterwards."

Luckily, a stage door at the side of the building had been left open and Garfield was able to nip inside. He found himself in a long corridor with doors on either side.

"This is like an adventure game on TV," he chuckled, starting to open every door in turn.

Some of the rooms proved very interesting. One contained lots of theatrical props and Garfield enjoyed a noisy mock swordfight. Another had racks of lavish costumes and Garfield laughed out loud as he dressed up as a German prince, a Greek warrior and an Egyptian queen. A third room was full of food and Garfield fell upon it with a whoop of joy. He took a huge mouthful.

"Ptooey!" he spat, "Pesky *fake* food! Tastes more like cardboard than Arlene's burgers!"

Eventually, there was only one door left.

"This must be the auditorium," thought Garfield, pushing it open.

In fact, he found himself in a posh dressing-room with a comfy couch, a table spread with drinks and nibbles and a big star's dressing-table in the corner.

"Must have known I was coming," chuckled Garfield.

Suddenly, there was a commotion outside the door and Garfield dived for cover amongst some boxes of powder and make-up. The opera singer in the helmet burst into the room, followed by a very worried theatre manager.

"This place is haunted, I tell you!" shrieked the woman, "I can't work here a moment longer."

"But you haven't finished the last act . . ." pleaded the manager.

"I don't care!" yelled the woman. "While I was on stage, I heard all sorts of dreadful noises underneath me – fighting, laughing and the most appalling eating!"

At that moment, the powder surrounding Garfield reached his nose.

"ACHOO!" he sneezed, leaping upwards.

The opera singer took one look at the cloudy white figure and fled from the building, screaming. And the manager fell flat on his face in a dead faint.

"I'm gonna be in trouble for this," thought Garfield, "unless . . ."

Back in the theatre, the audience was starting to get restless. The last act should have started ten minutes ago and the curtain was still down. Then there was a sudden flurry of activity in the orchestra pit as the musicians changed their music and the curtain finally went up, revealing a bare stage. Slowly, the trap door in the middle of the stage rose upwards and on it stood a familiar orange figure, holding a microphone.

"Hit it, boys!" yelled Garfield, waving his paw.

The orchestra struck up a chorus of 'Here Comes Garfield'.

What followed was the operatic performance of a lifetime. Garfield screeched and wailed louder than Kiri Te Kanowa with a spider down her neck. The audience loved it! They clapped and cheered and threw flowers onto the stage.

"These people have taste," said Garfield. "Normally, I get boots and shoes."

At the end of his recital, Garfield was given a standing ovation and forced to perform three encores. Jon's eyes filled with tears as he watched Garfield taking his final bow.

"And I thought Garfield disliked opera," he whispered proudly.

Later, in the foyer, Jon found Garfield signing autographs for a crowd of excited admirers.

"You were magnificent, Garfield," cried Jon.

"Not true," said Garfield, shaking his head. "I was *sensational*."

"You know I mentioned eating after the show," continued Jon, "How about making it a slap-up supper in the best restaurant in town?"

"That's music to my ears," laughed Garfield.

ALL STRESSED UP AND NOWHERE TO GO!

POOKY'S FAMILY TREE

THE STORY OF THE TEDDY BEAR

In 1901, Theodore Roosevelt became President of the United States following the assassination of William McKinley. President Roosevelt – known to most people as Teddy Roosevelt – was a keen hunter and, in 1902, he attended a Grizzly bear hunt in the state of Mississipi. No bears were sighted for several days and, in a desperate attempt to please their important guest, the organisers of the hunt imported a captive bear cub. To his credit, Roosevelt refused to shoot this defenceless creature and the incident prompted a cartoon that appeared in the 'Washington Star' newspaper on November 18th. It showed the President turning his back on a cute-looking little bear and bore the caption 'Drawing The Line In Mississippi.'

Picturepoint – London.

The cartoon was seen by **Morris Michtom** who, along with his wife, ran a small toy-making factory and shop in New York. Mrs Michtom made three soft toy bear cubs like the one in the cartoon and her husband sent one to the President, asking if he would object to the toy being called a 'Teddy Bear' after the hunting incident. Roosevelt replied, saying he did not mind the name being used but he did not think it would stimulate much business. How wrong he was! The first Teddy Bears with jointed arms and legs went on sale in America in 1903 and were an *instant* success. The Michtom's modest factory struggled to keep up with demand and, by 1907, they had expanded to become The Ideal Toy Corporation, one of the country's leading toy manufacturers.

Meanwhile, across the Atlantic, a similar phenomenon took place quite independently in Germany. At the Leipzig Trade Fair of 1903, a small family firm called **Steiff** exhibited a new jointed soft toy bear. Designed by Richard Steiff, who had seen some performing bears at a circus, it had been made by his aunt Margarete Steiff, a wheelchair-bound polio victim who had sewn soft toys all her life. These Steiff bears proved just as successful as their American rivals and, by 1907, the Steiff company were making a staggering 900,000 bears a year. These were exported all over Europe and the first Teddy Bears to reach Britain came from Germany.

The craze for Teddy Bears reached its peak before the First World War. By 1920 they had become an established part of childhood and most countries had their own toy bear manufacturers. The best known British firm was **Farnells** who produced top quality plush teddies sold in big toy shops and at Harrods. One of these Farnell Teddy Bears was bought for a little boy called Christopher Robin by his father, A. A. Milne. The bear was called Edward, but he went on to become the world's most famous Teddy Bear under a different name, Winnie-the-Pooh.

'The Bear of Very Little Brain' first appeared in a poem published in 'Punch' magazine in 1924. A. A. Milne then wrote two books, *Winnie-The-Pooh* (1926) and *The House at Pooh Corner* (1928) which established Pooh as one of the best-loved and most widely read children's characters since Alice in Wonderland. Pooh, Piglet, Kanga, Roo and Eeyore went on to delight an even wider audience when Walt Disney adapted their adventures into a classic cartoon film in 1966.

Three other fictional bears have rivalled Winnie-The-Pooh in terms of mass appeal. **Rupert,** invented by Mary Tourtel and continued by Alfred Bestall, has been a cartoon character in the 'Daily Express' since November 1920, inspiring countless annuals, books and even a hit song ('We All Stand Together') by life-long admirer, Paul McCartney. **Paddington Bear,** in his famous floppy hat, duffle coat and Wellington boots, was invented by Michael Bond in 1956. Dispatched from darkest Peru and found on Paddington station by the Brown family, this accident-prone little bear has amused generations of young children, both in books and on TV. Television has always been the home of **Sooty,** another mayhem-causing Teddy devised in the 1950s by Harry Corbett. Nowadays, Sooty, Sweep and Sue are managed (with the same degree of difficulty) by Harry Corbett's son, Matthew.

Pooky is the latest in this long line of Teddy Bear superstars. Given that GARFIELD is published in over 2,300 different newspapers around the world every day, Pooky is known and loved by millions of people. And Garfield does not mind sharing him with them. As he once said:

"POOKY IS A ONE-CAT TEDDY BEAR!"

Amazing Food Facts

Garfield, the world's ultimate foodie, presents some record-breaking facts about the subject closest to his stomach . . .

Made by Andreano Rossi of DOLMIO, Ciro Geroso and their team in Dublin.

VIVA LASAGNE!

The biggest lasagne ever made weighed an incredible 1637.3 kilograms (3609.61 pounds) and was 15.24 metres (50 feet) long and 1.52 metres (5 feet) wide. It was made at the Royal Dublin Society Spring Show in Dublin, the Republic of Ireland, on May 11th, 1990.

BANGER RACING

The longest continuous sausage on record measured a mind-blowing 21.12 kilometres (13.125 miles) – that's half the length of the London Marathon and a distance most people would only travel by car! It was made on the premises of Keith Boxley at Wimbourne near Wolverhampton in the West Midlands of England in only 15 hours, 33 minutes on June 18th and 19th, 1988.

ONE TO BE RELISHED

The largest hamburger in the world was made at the Outgamie County Fairgrounds in Seymour, Wisconsin, United States of America on August 5th, 1989. It weighed a staggering 2503 kilograms (5520 pounds), approximately the weight of 28 full-grown men!

PAST ITS SELL-BY DATE

The world's oldest cake is on display in the Alimentarium, a museum of food, in Vevey, Switzerland. It was found, sealed and 'vacuum-packed', in the grave of Pepionkh who lived in Ancient Egypt around 2200 BC. The cake measures about 11 centimeters (4.3 inches), has sesame on it and honey inside it, and was possibly made with milk.

AND FOR AFTERS . . .

The world's largest ice-cream sundae was made by Palm Dairies Ltd under the supervision of Mike Rogiani in Edmonton, Alberta, Canada on July 24th, 1988. It weighed a colossal 24,908.8 kilograms (54,914.8 pounds) and consisted of 20,270.7 kilograms (44,689.5 pounds) of ice-cream, 4394. 4 kilograms (9688.1 pounds) of syrup and 243.7 kilograms (537.2 pounds) of topping!

STRAWBERRY FOOL

The most expensive fruit of all time was not some exotic tropical rarity, but an ordinary punnet of strawberries auctioned at the Dublin Fruit Market on April 15th, 1977. John Synott from Ashford, County Wicklow, sold the 453 gramme (1 pound) punnet containing 30 berries for £530 – that's £17.70 a berry! The record-breaking price was paid by Leslie Cooke, a restaurant owner.

Extracts from: "The Guinness Book Of Records 1993"

Copyright © 1992 Guinness Publishing Ltd 1992.

ODIE'S PALINDROMIC PUZZLE

Odie may not know where the sky is or what his feet are for, but he can recognise a palindrome when he sees one. Can you do the same? Solve the clues, then see what all the answers have in common. One has been done for you as a guide and the answers are on page 61.

1. Eskimo canoe — KAYAK

2. Female sheep — EWE

3. Choirboys sing these on their own — SOLOS

4. Fruit seed — PIP

5. More and more red — HOTTER

6. Pop music concert or old-fashioned carriage — [ ][ ][ ]

7. Take a quick look — PEEP

8. An action, usually brave or daring — DEED

9. Something that rotates — ROTATOR

10. A joke or something to stop you speaking — GAG

11. Surveillance system used by aircraft and ships — RADAR

12. Horizontally flat — [ ][ ][ ][ ][ ]

13. Midday — NOON

14. A baby wears one for eating — B[ ]I[ ]A

15. Polite name for a lady, or a very naughty little girl! — MADAM

16. To paper a wall for the second time — [ ][ ][ ][ ][ ][ ]

17. Musical note lasting two beats — [ ][ ][ ][ ][ ][ ]

18. Long stories or adventure poems — [ ][ ][ ][ ][ ]

19. To mention, look for information or ask for someone's help — [ ][ ][ ][ ][ ][ ]

20. A young dog like Odie — [ ][ ][ ][ ]

ABLE WAS I ERE I SAW ELBA

20

Garfield's Favourite Cat Story

ANDROCLES and the LION

Many years ago, in North Africa, there lived a boy called Androcles. He was very kind and gentle, and loved animals. One day, Androcles tired of the noisy games of his friends and wandered off into the forest to look at the beautiful butterflies fluttering round the tropical flowers. There were so many vivid colours that he forgot the time and it began to grow dark.

"I must get home," thought Androcles.

It was too late. He lost his way in the gathering gloom and was forced to spend the night in a nearby cave.

Early next morning, Androcles was woken by the sound of crying. At first he thought another child was lost in the forest, but no one answered when he called out and there was something unusual about this crying. It was a sort of inhuman whimpering. As the bright African sunshine began to penetrate the darkness, Androcles spotted a lion cub huddling at the back of the cave. The little cat had a huge thorn sticking out of a front paw.

"You poor thing!" exclaimed Androcles. "Let me help you."

At first, the lion cub looked suspicious and growled defensively when Androcles tried to approach. So the boy began talking to the animal in a soft voice, pouring out a stream of soothing words to ease the tension. The cub realised that Androcles was a friend and allowed him to examine his wounded paw.

"This will only take a second," said Androcles, pulling out the thorn.

The lion gave a howl of joy and licked Androcles's face with his big, rasping tongue.

From that moment on, Androcles and the lion became firm friends. Every day, when he had finished his duties in the house, Androcles would hurry to the forest where the cub would be waiting for him. Sometimes they wrestled together; sometimes they played hide-and-seek amongst the thick ferns; sometimes they just sat together in the steamy noon-day heat. They seemed inseparable, but the young lion grew bigger all the time. The day came when he was not waiting for Androcles in the usual place. Androcles called and called, but the lion did not come. Nor did he return in the weeks and months that followed. The boy knew he would never see his friend again.

The years passed and Androcles, too, grew to be a man. One grey morning, a group of Roman soldiers arrived in the village, brandishing their swords. They were looking for slaves. Being young and strong, Androcles was one of the first to be taken and he soon found himself in chains on board a crowded slave ship bound for Rome. At the market, he was sold to a cruel master who beat him like a dog at every available opportunity. Every night, as he lay on his hard, wooden bed in the corner of the stables, Androcles dreamed of his home in North Africa and longed to escape.

One afternoon, his chance came. Androcles was told to pick grapes in his master's vineyard. The vines were a long way from the house and, when no one was looking, Androcles slipped away like a shadow. He waited until dark and then made his way out of the city, heading for the coast where he hoped to stowaway on a ship bound for Africa. But there were soldiers at the port, waiting for runaway slaves like Androcles. They soon recognised his short slave's tunic and recaptured him. In those days, the punishment for trying to escape was to fight without weapons against the wild animals in the Roman circus. So Androcles was taken away and chained to a prison wall to await his terrible end.

On the day of the circus, the huge Roman crowd gathered excitedly around the arena to watch their cruel sport. Down in the dungeons, the slave-master informed Androcles that he would be doing battle with Leo Magnus.

"He's our biggest lion," laughed the man. "We've had him for years and nobody has ever got the better of him."

Androcles cowered in the corner of his cell, trying not to think of the ghastly ordeal ahead of him.

Suddenly, a pair of rough hands yanked him to his feet, unlocked his chains and thrust him through a door. He found himself in the arena, dazzled by the bright sunshine after so many weeks of darkness. Then a door opposite opened and a great roar went up from the crowd as an enormous lion, his mane bristling and his teeth gleaming, bounded over towards him.

"How can I fight a beast like that?" thought Androcles, helplessly. He knelt down on the sand and abandoned himself to his fate.

Snarling ferociously, Leo Magnus paced up and down beside his victim. Through half-closed eyes, Androcles saw the great beast prepare to spring at him – and then change his mind. Everyone in the arena fell silent with astonishment as the huge lion padded over to the terrified slave, nudged him affectionately with his paw and began licking his face! "It's YOU!" gasped Androcles, recognising his long-lost friend from his days of childhood. In response, the lion rolled over on his back, inviting Androcles to tickle his tummy.

The crowd went wild with delight! They had never seen anything like this before. People were laughing and crying, clapping and cheering, waving and shouting. Then they began to chant, "Free him! Free him!" The Emperor bowed to their wishes. Summoning Androcles before him, Caesar declared that Androcles was no longer a slave and could go free.

"And I will grant you one wish," added the Emperor.

Without hesitation, Androcles replied:

"I want my friend, the lion, to be set free with me."

The wish was granted. To the further cheers of the crowd, Androcles and his lion walked out of the arena. They returned to North Africa where they lived peacefully together to the end of their days.

GARFIELD

WHERE
THERE'S
SMOKE,
THERE'S
FOOD!

LIFE IN THE

FAST - FOOD LANE!

A Winter's Tail

The streets outside were white with snow,
The pavements shone like mirrors;
An icy wind howled round the house,
Making Garfield shiver.

Suddenly, the doorbell rang.
Jon called out, "I'll go!"
Standing on the doorstep
Was a tiny mound of snow!

As the snow began to melt,
Two big eyes appeared;
Then a tail and a sweet pink nose,
Garfield thought, "How weird!"

"I do declare we've found a stray!"
Cried Jon (who likes to fuss.)
"You poor thing, come inside at once,
You can stay with us!"

"What's your name, kid?" Garfield growled.
"Perdita," replied the kitten.
Garfield felt his heart go BOOM!
By Cupid he'd been smitten!

Garfield raced round eating ferns
And gave Odie a shove;
"What's up, Garfield?" Jon exclaimed.
Sighed Garfield, "I'M IN LOVE!"

Perdita felt hungry,
So Garfield made a snack –
A sandwich full of goodies
Piled up in a stack.

"I can't eat that," the kitten mewed,
"I'm only small, you see."
"Just have a nibble," Garfield laughed,
"And leave the rest to *me!*"

Afterwards the cats played chase,
Then lay down by the fire.
"I like you, Garfield," Perdy purred,
Feeling warm and tired.

Garfield also closed his eyes,
But the doorbell rang again.
"Wake up, Garfield," Jon called out,
"You've got another friend."

In marched Arlene, looking fierce.
"What's going on?" she cried.
"I thought *I* was your girlfriend!
Obviously, you LIED!"

Arlene lashed Garfield with her tongue
And then gave him a whack.
"Goodbye!" she yelled, and slammed the door,
"I'm never coming back!"

Garfield shrugged his shoulders.
He didn't really mind.
"I've got a new love now," he smiled,
"And Perdy's more my kind."

DING-DONG, DING-DONG went the bell,
(For the third time that day).
"Look out, Garfield," chuckled Jon,
"Someone else has come to play."

Nermal strolled in, looking smart,
And cute as cute could be.
Perdita felt her heart go BOOM!
She whispered, "He's for me!"

Garfield watched in horror
As the kittens raced outside.
"Let's build a snowman," Nermal said.
"Yes, LET'S!" his girlfriend cried.

Garfield snatched some flowers,
But Perdita threw them away.
"No thanks, lardball," she cruelly sniffed,
"I'm afraid you've had your day!"

"Cheer up, Garfield," exclaimed Jon.
"Most women make you weep."
"I know," sighed Garfield," from now on
I'm only going to EAT AND SLEEP!"

I LOVE MY STUFF!

A QUIZ ABOUT GAMES AND TOYS

Answers on page 61.

1. In which popular board game can you buy London streets like Park Lane and Mayfair, take cards from the Community Chest or Go to Jail?

MONOPALY

2. LEGO, the construction toy, takes its name from a Latin phrase meaning what?
(a) Give it to me
(b) I build
(c) Where does this bit go?

3. Greek girls in the 5th century BC played with jointed dolls similar to those made today.
(a) True?
(b) False?

4. Which of these toys was a big craze during the 1950s?
(a) Hula hoops
(b) Spinning tops
(c) Gameboy

5. In which year was the game of Snakes and Ladders invented?
(a) 1770
(b) 1870
(c) 1970

6. Can you complete this sentence?
'Draughts is the British name for the game known everywhere else as ————.'

7. Which of these card games is the odd one out? Can you say why?
Bridge   Happy Families
Whist   Pontoon
Poker

8. Jigsaw puzzles, invented in the 1760s, were first made from what?
(a) Broken china
(b) Torn books
(c) Cut-up maps

9. How many pieces are there in a normal set of dominoes?
(a) 24
(b) 28
(c) 36

10. What is the world record for domino toppling by one man?
(a) Just over 10,000
(b) 212,467
(c) Nearly 300,000

11. What do these men have in common?
Gary Kasparov
Anatoliy Karpov
Bobby Fischer

12. Where were the earliest board games found?
(a) In an Egyptian tomb
(b) In the volcanic ruins of Pompeii
(c) Under Garfield's bed

13. Roman children were the first to play the game known as fivestones or jacks.
(a) True?   (b) False?

14. A radio controlled model helicopter has flown across the English Channel.
(a) True?   (b) False?

15. Hopscotch is an ancient game played all over the world. What does the word 'scotch' mean in the English name?
(a) A line scratched on the ground
(b) To fall over
(c) Chalk numbers
(d) My legs are facing in a different direction from my body.

16. What was the highest price ever paid for an antique doll?
(a) Just under £30,000
(b) £60,000
(c) Just over £90,000

17. In which well-known board game would you find the characters of Mrs White and Professor Plum?
Cluedo

18. Can you spell the name of the following toy – a tube or telescope containing mirrors and little pieces of coloured glass that makes beautiful patterns when twisted?

19. The game of Scrabble, first sold in 1948, was derived from what?
(a) Early-learning reading books
(b) Crossword puzzles
(c) School spelling tests

20. Which of these famous children's games does Garfield most like to play? Can you say why?
Musical statues   Dead fish
Musical chairs   Oranges and lemons
                  The farmer's in his den

Arlene's Calculator Criss-Cross

Arlene has a good head for figures. ("What's my waist measurement? How much does Garfield owe me?" etc). So here's a clever puzzle she has devised to test your skill at using a calculator. Solve the clues and fit the numbers into the grid, following the arrows for Across or Down.

Solution on page 61.

Across

A 22885 + 16890
E 5493 − 4523 − 896
G 77430 ÷ 87
H 82 × 85
I 14564 − 4743
J 100 − 75 + 50 − 25
K 3454 − 2756
L 1035 ÷ 45
N 69994 ÷ 886
R 1001 − 58
R 7 × 8
T 2235 + 2232 + 2069
U 7750 − 2466
V 859200 ÷ 960
X 3 + 3 + 3 × 6
Y 120+ 450 − 481
Z 4005 ÷ 89

Down

B 101 × 99
C 40132 + 20142 + 10613
D 244 × 23
F 320,000 ÷ 800
M 1256 × 2 + 1426
O 402 × 24
Q 11353 − 3914 − 2745
S 52 × 12
W 6452 − 3225 − 3172

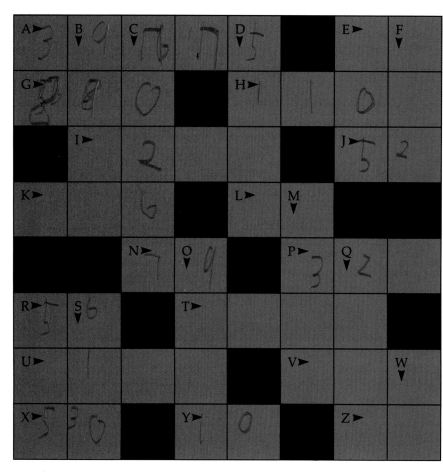

GARFIELD'S OPINION POLL

Jon had taken Garfield to see Liz the vet.

"Garfield's in perfect health," said Liz.

"Then why does he eat so much?" asked Jon.

"Because he's a fat, lazy, greedy cat," replied Liz.

"Steady on," put in Garfield. "Don't forget selfish!"

"I'm not so sure," mused Jon. "I think Garfield overeats because he's lonely. Odie's a loyal, friend but he's hardly Garfield's intellectual equal."

"This man's the master of understatement," muttered Garfield.

"So what are you getting at, Jon?" asked Liz.

"I need another pet to keep Garfield company," said Jon.

It so happened that Liz had the answer.

"I've been looking after this parrot for weeks and weeks," she explained. "He was brought in by a passer-by and no one's claimed him."

"But a bird's not a suitable companion for a cat," protested Jon.

"You wait till you see him," replied Liz.

Leaving Garfield reading the magazines in the waiting-room, Liz took Jon to the back of the surgery.

"Give us a kiss," said a high voice.

"Oh, Liz!" cried Jon, closing his eyes and puckering his lips. "How many times have I longed for you to say those words?"

"It wasn't me, you fool!" snapped Liz, "It was *him!*" The vet pointed to a large green and red parrot sitting on a perch.

"How do you do?" squawked the parrot. "My name's Duke, but you can call me Marmaduke for short. Ha, ha, ha!"

"He's a great talker," commented Jon.

"He's the cleverest animal I've ever met," said Liz. "That's why he'll be more than a match for Garfield."

Liz put Duke in a cage and Jon carried him back to the waiting-room.

"Meet your new companion, Garfield," called Jon. Garfield took one look at the bird and his eyes lit up with pleasure.

"What a surprise," he cooed, drumming his fingers together. "I think you and I are going to have *lots* of fun together."

As soon as they got home, Garfield went into the kitchen and started looking through Jon's cookery books.

"Parrot au vin, sounds nice," he muttered, "or parrot with orange sauce."

"Hope you're not thinking of being unkind to Duke," called Jon.

"Perish the thought," said Garfield.

"I think you'll be in for a nasty shock if you are," added Jon.

But Garfield was not listening. He was dreaming of a dish of parrot chasseur.

Later, when Jon went shopping, Garfield threw open the door of Duke's cage. "The direct approach is the best approach," he chuckled, thrusting his arm inside. Instantly, a wooden mallet descended onto Garfield's paw with the speed of light.

"YE-OWWCH!" he yelled.

"My anti-cat device with high-powered spring and infra-red sensors," explained Duke. "Doing very well on the export market."

"Glad to hear it," wailed Garfield, nursing his throbbing paw.

Garfield marched out to the garden shed and found Jon's fishing net. Hiding it behind his back, he returned to the lounge and sat casually in the armchair.

"Why don't you have a fly round the room," suggested Garfield. "Your wings must get stiff stuck in that cage all day long."

"Good idea," squawked Duke, fluttering out of the door.

Immediately, Garfield leapt to his feet and swiped at Duke with the net. But the parrot's reflexes were much too fast. He swerved aside and then dive-bombed Garfield with outstretched claws.

"YE-OWWCH!" yelled Garfield again.

"Learned aerial combat by studying the Battle of Britain," chuckled Duke, perching on the curtain rail and preening his feathers.

Garfield grew determined to get the better of Duke. He fetched a packet of sunflower seeds from the greenhouse and sprinkled them across the carpet as far as the door.

"Feather-features will follow the trail and then BINGO!" he giggled.

Garfield hid behind the door and waited. Sure enough, Duke flew down and began gobbling up the seeds. But he stopped before he reached the end and flew off to the kitchen. A few moments later, a delicious smell wafted under Garfield's nose.

"Lasagne!" he exclaimed.

Looking round, Garfield saw a line of mini lasagnes leading down the garden path. Without thinking, he devoured them one after another. As he bent over to pick up the last one, a sharp beak gave him a hefty peck and he leapt headlong into the pond. Just then, Jon returned from the shops.

"Glad to see you boys are out playing together," he chuckled.

"GLUG!" spluttered Garfield.

Garfield gave up any idea of catching Duke. Sensing victory, the parrot proceeded to bore Garfield rigid by talking incessantly all day long.

"Did you know I crossed the Sahara Desert on the wing of a Jumbo Jet?" said Duke.

"No," said Garfield.

"Would you like to hear all about it?" asked Duke.

"No," repeated Garfield.

The parrot opened one eye wide and raised a single claw.

"Y-Y-Yes," yelled Garfield. "Tell me the whole story ten times over!"

As the hours went by, Garfield grew more and more hungry, but Duke would not let him get anything to eat.

"You're fat enough already," he snapped.

Deprived of food, Garfield's brain went into overdrive. As Duke droned on about insect life in South America and the history of Chinese kite-making, an idea popped into Garfield's head.

"Sorry to interrupt," he said, "but how do I know you're not making all this up?"

"Because I read it in books!" snapped Duke.

"Parrots can't read," continued Garfield. "They just repeat things they've heard, like robots."

"That's what you think!" squawked Duke, indignantly. "Bring me something and I'll read it."

Garfield hurried across to the sideboard and fetched a pamphlet. As Duke gripped the pamphlet in his claws, Garfield picked up the telephone, dialled a few numbers and laid the receiver quietly on its side.

"Dial-a-dinner," said a faint voice at the end of the line. "What's your order?"

"Corn on the cob," read Duke in a loud voice. "Melon slice. Pepperoni pizza. Deep-pan lasagne. Burger and tomato sauce . . ."

"Keep going," whispered Garfield. "I shan't be satisfied until you've read the list right through twice."

Later, there was a knock at the door and a delivery man brought in a pile of food the size of Mount Everest.

"I didn't order all this!" gasped Jon.

"Somebody did, buddy," replied the man. "Are you paying cash or do you want to take out a loan?"

Jon looked furiously at Garfield who whistled innocently and pointed at Duke.

"He *must* be the culprit," exclaimed Jon. "He can talk!"

Jon took Duke straight back to Liz.

"I'm afraid he can't stay at my house a moment longer," he cried.

Returning home, Jon found Garfield already tucking into the food.

"Waste not, want not and all that," munched Garfield.

Jon looked suspiciously at his cat.

"I have a sneaking feeling," he said, "I'm being duped here. How did you learn to be so clever?"

"Parrot-fashion," chuckled Garfield.

GARFIELD

STRIPS

HALF A LASAGNE
IS BETTER THAN
NONE!

I think mice
Are rather nice.

Their tails are long,
Their faces small,
They haven't any
Chins at all.
Their ears are pink,
Their teeth are white,
They run about
The house at night.
They nibble things
They shouldn't touch,
And no one seems
To like them much.

But I think mice
Are rather nice.

Rose Fyleman

Garfield shares these sentiments, saying: "Show me a good mouser and I'll show you a cat with bad breath." If you're a mouse-lover too, turn the page for the lowdown on these loveable little fur-balls. (If you're a mouse-hater, fetch a chair and prepare to scream!)

Mice originated on the grassy plains of Asia. Over the centuries, they spread throughout Europe and have been carried by man to the Americas and Australia. They are now found in differing forms all over the world.

Like rats and certain insects, mice are one of the most common animals on earth. They breed at a phenomenal rate. Most types of mice are capable of reproducing at only three months old and females can have up to twelve young in a litter and several litters a year. So the world's total mouse population is impossible to estimate.

Mice are rodents. That means they are gnawing animals with a single pair of chisel-like teeth at the front of their mouths and none at the back. They can eat almost anything. Cereals like wheat and barley are their favourite diet, but they also eat protein foods such as cheese, nuts and meat. They have been known to eat chalk, soap, plaster, paste and glue!

As well as destroying food crops, mice can be a pest by spreading diseases such as typhus and plague. However, they perform a useful (and often unrecognised) service to man by providing the diet of other larger animals such as owls and foxes who would otherwise take more valuable food.

The **house mouse** (Mus musculus) is the most common sort of mouse and the one most people have seen. It is remarkably adaptable and can survive in the blazing heat of the tropics or the freezing cold of Antarctica. Its name comes from its fondness for sharing human dwellings, but these mice are equally at home in storage buildings like warehouses, rice paddies, fields of corn and sugar cane, marshes and coal mines.

Most house mice have brown-grey fur which is slightly paler underneath, large eyes and ears, and a pointed nose. They are 7- 10 cm (3-4 ins) long with a thick, scaly tail of about the same length. Males and females look very similar and are hard to tell apart.

The house mouse has poor eyesight, but acute senses of hearing, smell and taste. Its long whiskers are extremely sensitive and are used to guide it through narrow spaces. It is also a remarkably good climber with an incredible sense of balance, enabling it to run up and down walls, fences, pipes or anything vertical with ease. House mice are good at jumping considering their size, and they can also swim.

Picturepoint – London.

44

The **harvest mouse** (Micromys minutus), sometimes known as the 'red mouse' or 'red ranny' because of its russet-brown colouring, is one of the smallest mammals in Europe. A fully grown adult only measures 6-7½ cm (3 ins) and weighs a mere 6-8 grams (less than ⅓ oz). Harvest mice live in fields of cereal crops (hence their name) and feed off the grain, supplementing their diet with insects, butterflies, moths and caterpillars.

Because they are small, light and agile, harvest mice can climb and swing on the stalks of wheat and corn like mini-acrobats. Their tails are very important in this. When climbing, they twist them around the stalk and act like an extra foot; when descending, they use their tails like a brake. They build their nests amongst the stalks, sometimes as high as 1 metre (3 ft) above the ground. Their young are safer from predators there.

Picturepoint – London.

Harvest mice have many enemies. Weasels, stoats, foxes and even toads will attack them and they are the favourite food of the barn owl. Man, of course, disturbs their habitat when the cereal crops are cut down in the autumn and stubble-burning is another great hazard. Cold and wetness, however, are the greatest dangers – harvest mice are just too small to cope with bad weather. Despite all this, they continue to thrive. If you are lucky, you can spot them going about their business amongst the waving corn.

There are many other interesting and unusual types of mice. The **singing mouse** is so called because it emits a faint twittering sound that sounds musical. The **waltzing mouse** has an inherited faulty sense of balance and cannot move in a straight line. The **marsupial mouse** has a pouch for its young like the kangaroo to which it is related, while the **pocket mouse** has little pouches outside its cheeks in which food can be stored. The **white mouse,** which many children keep as pets, is a specially-bred variant of the house mouse.

FIRST PASTA THE POST

A board game for 2-6 players

You need a die, an eggcup for a shaker and some coloured buttons or tokens from another game as counters. Take it in turns to throw the die and get yourself onto the board. Then work your way around from 1 to 100. The tagliatelli spirals help you upwards, but the spaghetti slopes bring you down! Who will be the first to reach the Golden Lasagne?

Garfield's Guide to Christmas

Some useful advice about how to get the most from the festive season.

Your Christmas List

The importance of making a Christmas list cannot be exaggerated. Without one, people give you what they think you want, not what you *really* want. In order to cover every possible gift, your list needs to be about as long as the Bayeux Tapestry – and it must include a custard pie. (See 'The Aftermath' opposite).

Christmas Shopping

This is to be avoided at all costs. Browse through a mail order catalogue in the comfort of your armchair and select presents for all your friends. Write out the order list, but don't send it off. Then you can truthfully say you've ordered an expensive gift for everyone, and when it doesn't come you can blame the Christmas post. In this way, you'll earn lots of grateful thanks without ever parting with a penny. Or, if you prefer to elbow your way through the jostling, shouting crowd (and that's just the carol singers in the shopping precinct), remember this useful Christmas tip:
"Plastic is a Christmas shopper's best friend".

Christmas Cards

My advice is simple, but brilliant: send lots! Christmas cards are very useful for keeping people at bay. If all your boring neighbours receive a card, they are less likely to visit you over Christmas. In this way, you can preserve your precious supplies of Christmas goodies.

Carol Singing

There are two possible strategies here:

(a) Visit your neighbours in a small group and sing so badly that they pay you to go away.
(b) Go out in a large group, stand at the back and don't sing at all. You'll still get your share of mince pies and hot punch given by the people you visit.

Christmas Eve

The golden rule for Christmas Eve is BE A NUISANCE! Everyone's always so busy with last-minute shopping and final preparations that they'll give you *anything* to keep you quiet. You should be able to wangle all the chocolate decorations from the Christmas tree and your second or third best present a day ahead of schedule.

The other important thing to do on Christmas Eve is visit an airfield. For some unknown reason, Santa is supposed to put your Christmas prezzies in a stocking or pillowcase hung from the end of the bed. Both of these are woefully inadequate for the size and amount of gifts required. So, at the airfield, you might be able to persuade them to let you borrow an old windsock which is far better suited to the job. You will, however, have to sew up the big hole in the end.

Christmas Day

This is the only day of the year I get up early. Around 3 am is a good time. Santa has usually made his delivery by then and you can pitch into the parcels like a shark in a feeding-frenzy. It's best to play with your noisiest gift (a multi-sound ray gun or car with a siren) so that everyone else in the house wakes up and The Big Day can begin.

An interesting Christmas Day exercise is to see how long it takes your little brother or sister to break their best toy. Odie is brilliant at this. His stuff is smashed to pieces by breakfast time because he hasn't got a clue how anything works.

Around mid-morning, it's wise to start agitating for Christmas lunch. This has a habit of being late because the turkey isn't cooked or the sprouts are still hard. With consistent pressure, you should be in a position to pig out by early afternoon. This means you have the rest of the day to sleep and work up a ravenous appetite for supper.

Whatever happens, on Christmas evening, don't play any board or party games. These involve – horror of horrors – family conversation which should be avoided at all costs. With so many Christmas specials and blockbuster movies on all channels, it's your solemn duty to watch TV solidly until you get round to 3 am again.

The Aftermath

Never mind about all the weight you've put on and the bills you have to pay. They don't matter. The important thing is to be ready for the cornball who says: "Oh, well. Only 364 shopping days to Christmas."
That's when you splat 'em with the custard pie!

Boxing Day

People do strange things on Boxing Day like going to football matches and queuing for the January Sales. Don't be like them – be like me and sleep all day long. You've got to save your strength for demolishing all that cold turkey.

49

Where's Garfield?

There are 10 Garfields hidden in this jungle scene. Can you find them all?
Solution on page 61.

STRIPS

TAKE LIFE
ONE NAP
AT A TIME

PIZZA IS
MY LIFE!

THE BEST THINGS IN LIFE ARE EDIBLE

Back to the Fuchsia

  "Not bad," muttered Garfield, sitting on the dining room table and smacking his lips. "Quite a nice bouquet, but rather on the thin side for that particular year." Garfield jumped down and wandered into the lounge. He stopped beside the sofa. "What a beauty!" he cried. "Round and full-bodied, with just a hint of sweetness on the palate."

  Garfield was on a plant-tasting tour of the house. He worked his way from room to room, devouring every busy lizzie and geranium in sight. He left the fern in Jon's bedroom for last.

"This one's to be savoured," he drooled. "A classic vintage, light and fruity, with a delicious crispness that lingers on the lips."

  By the time Jon came in, every pot in the house had been stripped bare.

"I want a word with you, Garfield!" cried Jon.

"ME?" exclaimed Garfield, looking wide-eyed with surprise.

"You've been eating my houseplants again!" yelled Jon.

"Whatever . . . HIC . . . gives you that idea . . . BURP?" replied Garfield.

"You're a NAUGHTY, GREEDY, DESTRUCTIVE CAT!" roared Jon.

"Thank you," smiled Garfield.

"Sometimes," snapped Jon, turning on his heel, "I think about changing you for another pet."

"Wish you'd think about changing that shirt," replied Garfield.

Jon was wearing a hideous purple and white tie-dye shirt. He had made it himself many years ago and the die had dried in huge blobs that had not faded with the passage of time. It looked like a huge sheet of blotting paper.

"Stop making faces, Garfield," said Jon, picking up the telephone. "This is my favourite shirt and I'll wear it whenever I like. Now keep out of the way. I'm ringing Debbie."

"Not again," groaned Garfield.

Debbie was one of Jon's first girlfriends. They had been out on a date when they were teenagers, but then Debbie had moved out of the area. Now she was back, still single, and Jon was trying to date her again.

"*Why* can't you come to supper tonight?" Jon pleaded into the phone.

"Because you're a nerd," muttered Garfield.

"If you wash your hair tonight," continued Jon, "how about tomorrow night! Oh, you're going bowling. What about Friday night, then? I see, a disco. Saturday night?"

There was a slight pause.

"Gap in the girl's defences," commented Garfield.

"You're free, aren't you?" whooped Jon. "Come round at eight. I'll cook something special and you can see my new collection of tartan matchboxes. 'Bye!"

Jon slammed down the receiver and clasped his hands together in a frenzy of joy.

"She's mine!"

"And I own the Crown Jewels," murmured Garfield.

For the next three days, Jon was in a lather of activity getting ready for the big night. He mowed the lawn, weeded the flowerbeds, cleaned the windows, hoovered the carpet and polished the furniture several times over. Garfield felt very neglected, and now and again (every 10 minutes, in fact) he had to remind his master to feed him.

"Listen, Garfield," hissed Jon. "If this date's a success, I'll buy you everything on your Christmas list."

"Even the lifetime supply of frozen pizza with extra pepperoni?" exclaimed Garfield, pointing to the final item on his metre-long piece of paper.

"Even the lifetime supply of frozen pizza with extra pepperoni," agreed Jon.

"From now on, I don't exist!" cried Garfield. "But feed me first!"

At seven o'clock on Saturday evening, Jon decided the house looked bare and rushed out to buy some flowers. All the shops were shut, but he found a gypsy flower-seller just packing up her stall on the street corner.

"I'll take everything you've got," he cried.

"Only fuchsias left now, luv," replied the woman.

"They'll do fine!" exclaimed Jon, thrusting his money at her and rushing off.

"Mind the one with the bright red flowers . . ." called the gypsy.

But Jon was in too much of a hurry to heed the warning.

Jon had just finished arranging the pot plants around the house when he heard a deafening rumble.

"Sounds like thunder," gasped Jon.

"It was me, geek-features," said Garfield, pointing to his stomach. "I haven't eaten since tea time."

"No time to feed you now," snapped Jon, pushing Garfield into the other room. "I have to get ready for Debbie."

Garfield spied the bright red fuchsia on the coffee table.

"Problem solved," he grinned.

Opening his jaws like a JCB digger, Garfield ate the whole of the plant in a single chomp.

"GROH!" he spluttered. "It tastes DISGUSTING!"

Then Garfield's head began to spin. He held his paws to his ears and a billowing blackness engulfed him.

"W-W-What's happening?" he groaned, as the walls of the room faded away and Garfield found himself in the park. Everything looked different. People were wearing flared trousers and platform shoes and a song from 'Saturday Night Fever' was playing on a radio.

"Eating that flower's made me go back in time!" gasped Garfield.

A newspaper blowing around the park told Garfield it was the late 1970s. He had hardly absorbed this information when a familiar figure in an even more familiar shirt hurried into view, following a pretty teenage girl.

"I don't understand you, Debbie," cried Jon. "You promised to go boating with me, but now you say you have to meet Karen."

"Sorry, Jon," called Debbie, hurrying away. "Another time."

Garfield looked at his spotty-faced master-to-be standing with his hands held out and a crestfallen expression on his face.

"Wish I had a lasagne for every time he's looked like that," murmured Garfield.

Eager to find out what was going on, Garfield followed Debbie across the park. He watched her meet her friend at the bandstand and sneaked up to eavesdrop on their conversation.

"I don't like hurting his feelings, Karen," explained Debbie, "but how could I possibly be seen in public with someone wearing a ridiculous shirt like that."

"I know the feeling," thought Garfield.

Suddenly, Garfield's head began to spin again and the blackness returned. He closed his eyes and let himself go with the flow. When he opened his eyes again, he found himself back in the house with the calendar showing the present time. DING-DONG went the front doorbell.

"That'll be Debbie," chuckled Jon.

Garfield watched in horror as his excited master hurried down the hall in the blotchy tie-dye shirt.

"STOP!" yelled Garfield, leaping forwards.

With one raking blow from his famous claws, Garfield ripped the shirt from Jon's back.

"This is the last straw, Garfield," yelled Jon, racing upstairs to get changed. "I'm really going to get rid of you tomorrow."

Garfield let Debbie in and stood beside her grinning as Jon hurried back downstairs, tucking in a new designer tee-shirt.

"Thank goodness for that," smiled Debbie. "For one awful moment, I thought you might still be wearing that ghastly purple and white effort you were so fond of."

"But I . . ." began Jon.

Garfield kicked Jon on the shin and began flicking the pictures on the wall with the shredded remains of the shirt.

". . . er . . . use it as a duster now," added Jon.

"Glad to hear it," laughed Debbie. "You had really bad taste when you were young. I'm so pleased you've grown out of it."

The rest of the evening went very well. Garfield kept a low profile (very difficult with his figure) and was allowed to polish off the remains of the meal while Jon took Debbie home. Jon came back, bubbling with excitement.

"Debbie says she might see me again sometime," he chuckled.

"Beauty but no brains," commented Garfield.

"And it's all thanks to you, Garfield," added Jon. "I wouldn't change you for the world."

"Brains but no beauty," said Garfield.

Next day, Jon kept his promise and bought Garfield everything on his Christmas list.

"What I don't understand," said Jon, tipping out the huge pile of parcels, "is how did you know Debbie didn't like that shirt? You must have some special psychic power."

"More like flower-power," smiled Garfield.

ANSWERS

Odie's Palindromic Puzzle *(page 20)*

1. Kayak
2. Ewe
3. Solos
4. Pip
5. Redder
6. Gig
7. Peep
8. Deed
9. Rotator
10. Gag
11. Radar
12. Level
13. Noon
14. Bib
15. Madam
16. Repaper
17. Minim
18. Sagas
19. Refer
20. Pup

Palindromes are words that read the same whether you look at them backwards or forwards.

I Love My Stuff *(pages 32 and 33)*

1. Monopoly
2. (b) I build
3. (a) True
4. (a) Hula hoops
5. (b) 1870
6. Checkers
7. Happy Families. It requires a special pack of picture cards whereas the other games are normal playing cards.
8. (c) Cut-up maps
9. (c) 28
10. (c) Nearly 300,000
11. They are all World Chess Champions
12. (a) In an Egyptian tomb
13. (b) False. (The game was first played by the Ancient Greeks.)
14. (a) True
15. (a) A line scratched on the ground
16. (c) Just over £90,000
17. Cluedo
18. Kaleidoscope
19. (b) Crossword puzzles
20. Dead fish. It requires you to lie perfectly still!

Arlene's Calculator Criss-Cross *(page 34)*

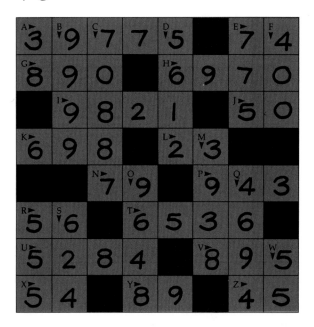

Where's Garfield *(pages 50 and 51)*

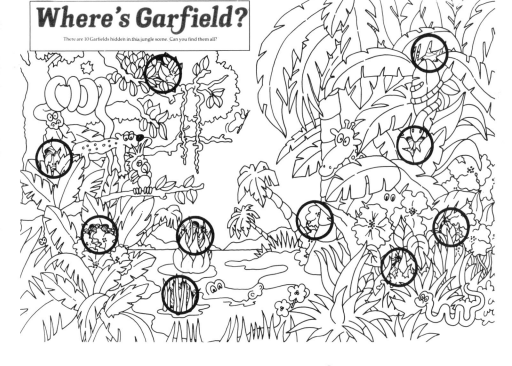

Where's Garfield?
There are 10 Garfields hidden in this jungle scene. Can you find them all?